MW00777762

ZEN PSYCHOSIS

ZEN PSYCHOSIS

Shana Nys Dambrot

Photographs by Osceola Refetoff

Griffith Moon

Zen Psychosis
Shana Nys Dambrot
Copyright © 2019 Griffith Moon. All rights reserved.
No part of this publication may be duplicated or
transmitted in any form without prior written consent
from the Publisher. Displaying such material without prior
permission is a violation of international copyright laws.

ISBN: 978-1-7326992-8-1

Photographs by Osceola Refetoff
Book Design by Sara Martinez
Printed in the United States of America
First Printing, 2019
Published by Griffith Moon
Santa Monica, California
www.GriffithMoon.com

RANCE

GOOD EVENING

1

I had fallen asleep on a blanket at the beach, next to my lover, very close to the water.

It was a dark and oily place, on the shore of a great greasy sea filled with the bloated carcasses of the drowned, glowing white in the moonlight. It was awful. I kissed my lover quickly, thanking God for him. He looked at me with tender indulgence—he still loved my craziness then. He suddenly stood and began to throw his books at me, prodding me to get up so he wouldn't be late for his afternoon meeting.

As I reluctantly rose to my feet, I saw mountains in the distance framing his beautiful golden face and eyes the same color as the bruised blue sky. There were overlapping V-shaped clouds projecting up from behind the mountains and out across the bay. The clouds were long and thin, like steamed spring rolls in rice paper, arranged like a grove of palms on a hilltop. He turned to look, and as I followed his gaze, I saw that the clouds were in fact palm trees on the crest of the green hill unrolling above us, and below was not an ocean at all, but an empty parking lot.

The next time I saw my lover, he was seated, with his back to the doorway, on a long blue leather sofa in the Reading Room at the Blackstone Library. Though it was early afternoon, there was a glowing fire in the hearth he faced. It was utterly silent, as though the entire building were wrapped in cotton, and he was alone there. He did not hear me sliding across the polished marble floor, engrossed as he was in his reading. I came up behind him and looked over his shoulder. His gold-rimmed glasses reflected firelight so that I could not make out his eyes, but he took them off to turn and smile at me. It felt sincere.

He was reading the I Ching, the edition with the forward by Carl Jung. It was odd, because I realized the copy he was reading I had borrowed from him. I wondered how it could be that he had come back into possession of it. I had no memory of returning it to him, although I knew my own —the one I bought so he could have his back— had been recently misplaced.

He stayed in that room, while I returned to the rotunda, and craned my neck to consider the scenes painted on the inner face of its dome. The Global History of Books unfolded across the ceiling, from Ben Franklin's first press to Egyptian papyrus-printing techniques, complete with a seated scribe and Thoth the patron saint of knowledge, looking it over. I wanted to tell my lover about Thoth, as we had had some interesting escapades in the name of that particular exiled deity. Forbidden knowledge of astrology and mathematics is no joke, it'll get you kicked out of the pantheon and marooned on a mountaintop in South America in the blink of a millennial eye.

I jumped when my lover called out to me from the couch. He had turned on the sofa, and was leaning his head on his hands across the back of it in the most endearing

way, to watch me draw near. At first he only looked at
me, long and hard, as though he were seeing me for the
first time. He asked me out loud, How many times have
we met before, I mean in previous lives? And when he said
it I saw it, all of it. In deepest darkest Peru I saw snakes
and lizards; I felt the steam on my face and heard monkeys
singing in the trees. We wandered through literary salons
and cheap cafés from Paris to Amsterdam. I was Gertrude
Stein. He said, do you remember the hotel in New York?
With all the roaches but we didn't care because we had each
other. I was Lucretia Borgia, Marilyn Monroe, a milkmaid
from Vermeer, a courtesan at the time of Manet. I was a
butterfly. I was a virgin, a witch, a Lilith. I said, I love you,
and called him by his name. He said, I love you, too.

2

Enter the scene in medias res: a cramped office, crowded with people who resemble my former colleagues. The room is fluorescent-lit, giving it a nauseous sterility that the aqua blue Deco chairs, fake wood paneling, and chipped Formica coffee table only exacerbate. The apparent leader of the meeting is a regal African woman in a sarong and wooden beads. She evinces pronounced disinterest in both my presence and an article written not by but about me which had appeared in that day's paper. The paper in question lay on the coffee table unruffled, my own face staring back at me from above the fold. It was a very crowded and tense little room; stale air with no ventilation and no windows. A hot night.

While I was trying to catch up with what was going on in the meeting, I remembered how I had gotten there. I had left my car in the parking garage and taken a bus to the meeting. Instantly upon forming that thought, I was back on the bus, just stepping off at a strip mall on Hamburger Hill that I recognized from my hometown in Connecticut. It had the Gap from which I was fired in high school. The night was growing hotter.

I retraced my path on foot, thinking that I needed to return to the meeting for some reason. I was feeling annoyed at having left so abruptly, but nevertheless relieved to be gone. A heavy sense of obligation was shuffling my feet back that way. Soon, an old man, bald with a white mustache, fell in step with me and we began a conversation. That is, I could see him speaking though no words were audible—a fact which I did not realize until I later tried to recall the conversation and found I could remember only the scene, not the dialogue, like watching a film with the volume turned all the way down. Just as I was going to address him by his name, I realized he was not the person I thought he was. I was relieved not to have called him aloud by the wrong name, but then who was this guy?

Still trying to remember, I arrived alone at my grandmother's house, and descended into the finished basement. Finished 45 years ago. Round wooden table with carved legs, beige knotted silk sofa, gold velveteen easy chair, ceramic cat bent in contemplation of an imaginary fish pond, irregularly shaped green glass vases and watercolors of the local piers by talented amateurs. The same dusty sunlight through the clerestory windows for 45 years. One thing was new—a rather large and frightening brown hairy spider. As I approached, it scurried between the pages of a ragged copy of Thus Spake Zarathustra, so I closed the book, killing it. I paused for a moment to care that the now-stained book belonged to my lover, but I was out the door into the afternoon.

I set out walking toward downtown L.A. on Centinela but much too far West, on a mercifully shady street. I could see Downtown in the hazy distance of smoggy afternoon sun. I suddenly felt quite thirsty, and so I left the road to walk up a dirt driveway to a concrete bungalow, where I thought I might find some water to drink. I saw as I was admitted that the cottage was cavernous inside, with wood floors and sparsely furnished with a beanbag and a pile of pillows in the center of the room. A couple lived there, middle aged man and young wife. All their things were packed because they were moving to Japan the next day. They needed to raise $50,000 cash before they could go, but they didn't seem worried about it. They gave me cereal in milk instead of water, and I saw that the man was not the old man from earlier, but in fact he was the man for whom I had mistaken the older one when I'd met him in the road.

We walked outside together just as the first old man pulled up in my car, which he had retrieved from the parking garage. It irritated me a bit at first that he had taken the liberty of driving my car, but I soon realized that was petty, and I should be thrilled to have it for the rest of the trip Downtown inside a seamless, never-ending, sultry afternoon.

3

Two more journeys on foot up Hamburger Hill, in my hometown, and also freshly snaking its way through Main Street, Santa Monica. I was in search of concert tickets for Nick Cave at the venue up the hill. I had one minute to make it all the way from a restaurant in my neighborhood by the beach. I was already irritated because I had paid twenty dollars for a pizza that two of my friends had eaten entirely without me. Plus I had one minute to walk miles.

I set off with the memory of my last walk on this path still fresh in my mind, and just like before, each step was excruciatingly heavy and slow. I couldn't breathe, I could barely force my feet to move, even at a crawl. It was like I was in a dream, walking under water. I reached for every brick and doorknob along the shop fronts to propel myself forward, like a horizontal rock climber, or a drunk. Buses went by, both transit and school, but still I stubbornly kept walking.

A former employer was watching a tiny neighborhood Italian place for a mutual friend. I saw her sitting on a table top by the bar, and detoured through the place. I sneaked a fried shrimp off a passing tray, and kept moving. I never made it back up the hill that day. The sun went down and my labors faded into shadow.

Defeated, I took a shortcut home through the park without really deciding to. Rabid squirrels were coming at me in military formation. Littering the ground were several heavy and shiny steel locks. Adrenaline suggested I swing them at the little monsters to fight them off. I was in underwater motion again, like earlier when I had to get up the hill in and could barely walk at all. I swung a lock at one, but I missed somehow, in spite of the close range. It bit my inner thigh with a vengeance and wouldn't let go.

Down the street from the park was an abandoned theater, where I ducked in to catch my breath and examine my wounds. It had a bar in the lobby built on an aquarium, all chrome and tiny bubbles. There was a terrace off one side, and on it was a baby in a shopping cart. She wanted her bottle, but never cried for it. I stumbled out to the terrace while frantically running around corridors backstage, trying to find a way to sneak into the show.

I dove back inside the building, and just then some curtains parted in my path, and I entered from the side of the crowd. The sea of people was illuminated like a sunset by red and blue lights from the stage. Smoke had gathered overhead and trapped the light beams.

I found myself turned around yet again, back out on the terrace, watching the baby. I called her by my sister's name, and she looked up at me through a hole in her blanket. Our eyes locked. Someone was making a scene in the park across the street. No place for a baby. But where were her parents? I knew I could never raise her on my starving artist salary, so I left her there to go look for qualified help.

4

I was working at that time as the only waitress in a cavernous, noisy, cheap dining hall. Long rows of folding tables and chairs, like a bingo palace. Families with screaming children, couples with nothing to say to each other, octogenarians remembering the War with uneasy fondness. I ran in circles for hours, and only managed to order like five drinks and one dish of spicy Thai noodles. I just circled the tables, expecting to get yelled at for incompetence at every turn. I kept gliding around, and eventually I got my chance to escape. I waited until I was sure no one was watching me, and headed for the front door.

Outside, my lover waited for me in the car. I could see the red light of his cigarette, and his hand tapping the wheel to a beat. As I approached, the engine roared to life, the passenger door opened toward me, and I heard the music blasting from inside. We were in motion before I closed the door, laughing until we thought we would never stop.

As we raced down city streets, dark and glittering after the evening's rain—rain makes everything in New York look silver—I got cramps and my period started. Sublime pain, almost blinding, but the pain subsides right away. I privately thanked god for the pain, though, as that is better than the alternative.

Again I find myself turning this scenario around and around in my head. My lover does not want a baby. Neither do I. But we love each other, and if I get pregnant now, it's like we would almost be happy, but it's a bad idea and we're not ready. I know an abortion is the right thing to do, but worry it would ruin the casual easiness of our love. I've seen it happen so many times. A man can struggle to make love to woman who has aborted his child, even with his blessing and support; after such drastic action to avert what might be destiny. But here is the blood flowing, and there's no need to worry over this tonight.

5

Walking alone, on my way to Skinny Binny, the all-night pet store, I'm in a bad part of town. There was about to be an earthquake, and I was trying to stock up on pet supplies. A group of boys passed me, and a tall one grabbed a yellow and black street sign off a pole, bumping me with it. I walked a little faster. The light from the pet store glowed from around the corner as I came out of the alley into the parking lot and street. The completely deserted parking lot and street.

My lover appeared and silently linked arms with me. He gently and safely guided me to his townhouse, through the rooms and out the back door to a courtyard where an art event of some kind was being held. Warm, genteel, with heat lamps on the patio. Instinctively I pulled my hand from his arm, but he stopped me. He said he no longer cared who saw us together. We were in love, and he kissed me, a long soft kiss right in front of everyone. It had the texture of a wish.

I became pregnant with his baby, and he comes around in this expensive black suit and says, I love you, baby, but I think he really does just mean the baby and not me, its vessel. It pisses me off and I jump out of my seat on the top of the Double Decker bus; looking down through the flooring, I can see there are two drivers. They were arguing about which direction to go. The handrails were too far apart, too easy to fall through. Bad design, as bad as having two drivers. I recall an urgent need to get off that bus.

Back in my own car, I almost laugh and think it must have been Crazy Driver Day and no one told me. I narrowly missed about 20 accidents just on my way home from the museum. While I was thinking about being lucky, I pulled into a parking lot. Another car had just pulled in ahead of me. It was an old Mercedes, like a '71 or '72. The driver was an older woman, very conservative and a little spaced out. She was stopped right there, right in my path, but I did not hit the brakes. I was paralyzed and could not do it, and my car made a loud thud as it hit hers. She looked at me over her shoulder out the window, but did not get out. Her tall bitchy friend in the Chanel suit got out instead, and eyed me suspiciously as we surveyed the damage. I offered to pay for her repairs, but nothing had really happened to either car, so we just dropped it and drove off in different directions. As it turned out, we both had better things to do.

6

Joy-riding. This is what we were accused of by Ken Doll CHiP, the motorcycle cop with the blue eyes and cleft chin. It was an accusation I felt was particularly ironic, since joy was the farthest thing from my reality by the time we were stopped. We had been going too fast by half, and I was terrified. I was doing my best to hide my fear with sarcasm, but our reckless speeding on a dark two-lane road with no fence for protection against the drop down to the river on the right was getting to me. It had been exhilarating for around 30 seconds, but we were now out of control.

Ken Doll arrested them all while the car was still in motion, though at a greatly reduced speed, leaving me alone in the passenger seat while they were spirited away. The car was giving itself a little gas, still moving forward despite having no driver. I was attempting to steer from the passenger side, but I was not doing a very good job. By this time, the sun had come out and climbed high overhead. The light had a soft green filter on it, like tea falling across the road's surface.

I started to lose my bearings going around a steep curve on an incline. I was falling asleep in my seat, but the car was still wide awake. Just as my eyes were closing, I looked to my left and saw Ken Doll's beautiful plastic face, looming slightly larger than life out the driver's side window. His face was tan and smooth, with no lines at all except deep creases where his cheeks folded in laughter. Stern set to his jaw, and a level stare. He had a sort of friendly manner backed up by physical power. His eyes, I keep going back to them. Those eyes could stop a raving madman cold with just a look.

He was not there to arrest me. I tried to slip over the driver's side, but he had, of course, already taken the wheel. As soon as he reached in through the window, the car slowed to a gentle stop on the shoulder, and I got out. We two were standing at the head of a wide trail which sloped away from the road, downward toward a pool at the base of a waterfall. None of it could be seen from the road, especially from a moving vehicle. Around the water's edge were wooden platforms accessing various areas of the rocks and falls. My friends were playing there like children, nowhere near jail. It was so obvious to me in that moment that Ken Doll (I was starting to feel guilty for calling him that, even only in my head) and I were destined to meet, had already always known each other.

He started to walk me down the path, with his strong arm at my back. The light touch of his fingertips on my spine was enough to move me with no fear of slipping or falling. I was preparing for the reactions of my group to seeing us enter together, after the scene on the road earlier. But before we even got that close, he stopped walking. It took me a moment to realize he was saying good-bye.

7

It really started here in this bed at 2am. The fan on the window sill is pointed outward, to draw out the smoke from the joint, and it makes the frail glass lamp on the nightstand purr in rhythm. The shimmer effect is distinctly Southern, like the traces of shadows a ceiling fan would make in a Tennessee Williams play. Breezes and old mirrors, wooden bed posts at the head and baseboards, lacy duvet covers, blue chambray sheets, a feather mask from a genuine New Orleans Mardi Gras with a red flame pattern on it, and next to that a tapestry hangs on the far wall, a bald eagle gripping red and blue pennants with stars and stripes. It's supposed to be pre- or neopost-Revolutionary, but it looks positively Confederate.

Before my grandfather died, I shared this bedroom with my mother. We had twin beds in the largest room, the one at the end of the hall, upstairs in my grandparents' house. There's only one bed in there now, a big creaky old four-poster maple bed, just a little too high to sit down on. I have to climb up into it, even as an adult. The view from the pillow is straight out and up into the sky through the branches of the oak in the front yard. This is the room where I sleep when I visit her now, if you call this nocturnal demon hunting sleeping.

Without any warning, I am swept out to sea in the irresistible wake of a huge round rock. It carries me straight out into Long Island Sound, away from the familiar neighborhood beach where my mother and grandmother stand dumbstruck. I start to scream when I see the two of them standing there, so utterly powerless. They looked so small, two black specks standing stock still, while the dog-speck ran back and forth, in a pitiful pantomime of helping. The great sweep of sandstone jetty flung wide its arms as I backed out at top speed; the boulder whose gravity held me close was made of the same mottled rock. The houses looked so insincere, all laid out in a pretty row. Hedges looked soft and friendly from a distance, but the fragrant flowers were hiding sharp metal fences. I expected the open sea to be quiet, but it was thunderously loud, deafening, in fact. And hot as hell, even in the water.

I didn't go swimming much after that.

8

From where I sit at my desk by the window, I can see the sunset everyday except for two and a half weeks in December. The sun moves a fraction of an inch every 24 hours; it slips south between July and December, and creeps north again January through June. Along the way it stops at the red brick chimney, the satellite dish, the roof of the blue house, the cedar shingles, the Frank Gehry townhouse, the flat-topped apartments with the potted trees and the lawn chairs, and the silhouettes of people drinking martinis while they watch the sunset, too.

For two weeks each November and again in February, it sinks directly into the ocean through a gap between roof tops. From May to August it is way up north behind the mountains. This has an odd effect because these are the longest days of the year, yet it seems to set earlier than ever because of the outcroppings. But I can see the ridges clearly all the way east to the Hollywood sign; it's like my own private sunset from the balcony. And then maybe half an hour later—when the sun really does set though it's already out of view—the whole sky swells up with color. It's like the secret bonus track way at the end of a cd, that you only hear if you are too stoned to get up and change it when it first ends. An inside joke, shared with the universe.

And in all these years I have never seen the ocean look the way it did last night. It was like a revelation. I felt like I was seeing the moon for the very first time. The full moon's wide beam ran straight toward us on our hilltop. It's the same hill that hides the sun early in Summer, but now we were on its crest. The water was far from serene, neither still nor glassy. It absorbed the light like a canvas; it was not a mirror. There weren't waves so much as vibrations, like gooseflesh, or fabric in a breeze.

Shadows moved across it and I saw visions. There were two dozen people drumming in the rotunda behind me, while my eyes crossed and revealed what the shadows hid. Migrations of animals across Sub-Saharan Africa, with gazelles and rhinos and monkeys and big cats all being followed by hunters. There were also modern folks playing in the surf along the shore. They were laughing and playing with beach balls and I thought, I am watching people now that have drowned in that spot across the years.

The drums stopped suddenly on a sharp beat, the animals stopped running, the people swam away. I heard the waves crash then for the first time all evening.

9

On the beach again, back at the same spot where I always go to think something through. On that particular afternoon, a Monopoly board was being coaxed out to sea by the fingers of an advancing tide. My driftwood perch is not far from the wet edge, and I have to yank my feet back from a few precocious waves. I had cuts on my feet, and the salt water made them sting. It wasn't long before I was forced to return to the house.

I had had a fight with my father, the cause of which I had already forgotten, in our apartment below the Rainbow Room. Our place was a skirt of glass around the building, like a diamond necklace on an old society dame. We came in the same doors as the talent and crew entrance for the club on the ground floor, past the bouncers, always a velvet rope on the way home. We had a private elevator at least. Apparently I had said something inappropriate to my father while we were watching the sun set over New Jersey, because the next thing I knew, we were at it again.

I have no doubt that my comments were uncalled for, and my guilt only inflamed my rebellious rage. I threw a bag of flour at him in the kitchen, because he was wearing a black cashmere sweater and hated the contact of the organic and inorganic. I figured, correctly as it turns out, that he would be distracted by the ruined sweater long enough for me to make an exit. I ran out barefoot, and shredded one heel on some rocks in the parking lot. Finally I made it to the beach, where I had been sitting until the tide came in. As I turned to leave, I remembered that salt water is supposed to be curative, and braced myself for one last rush of water, which hurt like hell, but I knew it would help.

I gave up on the impulse to go home, and turned back to face the ocean. Some dolphins were out in the waves breaking on the sandbar. I waded in to try to get their attention. What I found instead was that I was extremely late for class, staring straight ahead at the closed door to Room 23, hearing my mother's voice begin the lesson, weighing my options. She opened the door just as I was turning to go.

Class was such a bore on that day, I mean more than usual. It was almost the end of summer vacation, and my interest had been waning since October. All I was good for was staring out the window at the ocean, sunset coming on, water flat and silent like silver satin sheets. My mind wanders to the highway, to the events of the night before. We got stuck and had to be rescued, bailed out of jail, just a week before graduation. A skinny boy who had loved me for years and to whom I had been unbelievably cruel for just as long, came to help me. I could see him already down at the water, waving me to follow him. I never would, of course.

10

A massive Monarch butterfly with a strong body and a distinct head like black chenille came to rest on my left index finger. It crawled around on my left hand and forearm for what seemed like hours, even as I went about my business in town.

It stayed with me when I stopped at the beachfront hotel bar to track down a friend who had promised to give me a lift to school that day. It was a promise that became more and more precious to me as the rain came harder and harder. I was utterly dismayed to run into my grandmother in the lobby. Apparently, she was vacationing there with a friend of hers, who happened to have been a math teacher at my High School. With them was my uncle (by marriage, to my grandmother's other daughter) though the aunt was not present.

See, the problem with the situation was this: no one in my family ever knew that I had not actually graduated from High School. I had managed to graduate from college legitimately, but years later I wanted to finish High School for myself, for satisfaction, or maybe just for kicks. In any case, it was definitely a secret from my family. My dear friend didn't know any of this, he was just giving me a ride to the school, but he assumed I was teaching! Anyway, my grandmother overheard him saying, "blah, blah, blah, leave for school now." She asked me what was going on, but I pretended not to hear her question, and split. Butterfly still hanging on.

It was gone, though, that butterfly, the next time I remember checking, as we pulled up in front of the school building. This friend had commandeered a city bus somehow, but he didn't know its route. I offered to show him, since it pretty much matched the way to the school anyway. He let me out and drove on, and that's when I noticed the butterfly was gone.

On the drive over, the rain had gotten even harder, and the sky darker. As soon as I got off the bus, I ducked under a tree to prepare for the dash across the street, up the wide stone stairs, and in through the heavy cast iron doors. On the other side of those immense doors was a damp and musty flagstone foyer. While I carefully plotted my course through the deepening puddles, my lover appeared at my side.

We kissed and sighed, hello you. I began to go over in my mind whether I really had to go to school at all that day. True, I had been out most of last week; and true, I had prepared an oral presentation which I was expected to deliver that afternoon. But the warmth amid all the chill made it truly difficult to take action. It was the kind of day that would be perfect for making love to someone for the first time.

I glanced at the sidewalk with my head resting on my lover's shoulder, as the black high heel of a passerby's shoe crushed one of three monarchs on the ground. They were drenched or even drowned from the rain. The sight, and even years later, the memory, engulfed me with sadness, and broke the spell. I turned away from him, holding back tears, and headed toward the school.

11

High School in the big city. My sweetheart then is my lover of today, exactly as he is now. We walk together into the cafeteria where everyone is assembled. There is one girl in particular, with short blond hair in a plaid mini skirt like at a Catholic school. She obviously covets him, having no respect for me at all in the way she throws herself at him. He and I were standing face to face in the middle of the room holding hands, and she walks straight up and gets in between us. Throws her hands around his neck and stands there talking up into his big beautiful face like I didn't exist.

This is what they call the last straw. I clear my throat and step close to her, mystified by his lack of response to this affront. He has still made no move to back away. I pulled her off of him by the hair on the back of her head, like peeling a cat off the upholstery. Dragged her a few feet to the closest table and pounded her forehead down onto the Formica with a whoosh and a dull splat thud. She crumpled to the floor in tears. I took his hand and led him out of the building. No one took any notice.

On the city bus with the green school bus seats we took toward home, we talked the incident over a little. He sat behind me, so I had to turn in my seat to look at him. All through the crowded downtown section, the neon signs began to blur in the mist that was fast becoming rain. It was this part of town that I had fallen in love with so many years ago when I came here, lost. I finally moved here, around the time I met him.

The bus pulled into the gravel driveway of a Veterans Administration bowling alley and some vets boarded. Slight smell of cigarettes and spilt beer. My lover was in the middle of saying, "What was the big deal? It's not that serious between me and you anyway, right?" I said that, no, he's right, it's not that serious. But my heart was broken. He went on to say he might very well date her sometime. When I heard that, I said nothing, only got off at the next stop, two short of mine.

I couldn't wait to get outside into the blessed wet rain, where it would be harder to tell I was crying. If I could just get off the bus without him seeing my face, I'd have an alibi for the smudged mascara. The bus slowed, I rose unsteadily and exited without turning around once. I admit I was half listening for his steps behind me, but they did not come. I heard the doors slide shut behind me, heard the bus pull away from the curb. I thought I heard him calling from the window, but I couldn't be sure.

I hadn't gone more than 100 feet when I heard him distinctly, calling my name and coming closer. He reached out and touched my shoulder, spinning me slowly to face him. I think the rain was only partially hiding my emotions. In silence he pulled me in close to him, one hand on the small of my back strong and warm. After a moment, he guided me down the street. He looked shocked and concerned. At home, my home, the first thing he said was, "I had no idea I meant this much to you."

I said, "Neither did I."

12

An art show in the LBC, a horrible installation by a former lover. He had run plastic tubing around the perimeter of the rooms, floor and ceiling. Clear industrial plexiglass, thousands of yards of it. The tubes were running with red water like blood. There were diagrams of my old lover's plans to install such tubes around the steps of the Capitol Building in Washington.

I was there with the gallerist, but the artist was in Europe. For whatever reason, I was attempting to resuscitate her impression of the show. I kept trying to tell her that since he was out of town, someone else must have assembled the piece, obviously it wasn't done by an artist. The room was thick with pot smoke, and people saying things like, I'm not an artist anymore, I've given it all up. Things like, Modern man is a lost cause.

My lover finally arrived in a cloud of hangers-on. Seeing him after all this time, I rushed to the loo in a haze of memories, to apply blood red eyeliner. I thought it looked beautiful. In a grotesque way, it was, but it better served art than a human girl.

Thank goodness the next party was at the Episcopalian rectory, where the minister was the artist's mother. A pot luck dinner, where I had planned on seeing more of him. Distractions included the appearance of a few former roommates. The one especially, the one who had dropped it all to marry a Mexican sculptor and have his children, she looked as I remembered her to look from a distance. As I approached she began to look more and more like me.

Asking her questions about Mexico, I did not notice when my lover finally arrived, wearing nothing but some dirty brown corduroys. His shoulders were stooped and covered in a light fuzz of red hair. His pants were unbuttoned, and he was staring at the television. He would not talk to anyone except to ask when dinner would be ready. My friend thought he was a homeless person that had come to the Rectory looking for help, and was prepared to feed him. I took her aside and set the record straight. Knowing they had just started cooking, I left to get him something to eat from my place.

When I returned, everyone had left to see our friend's band at some club downtown. I was alone in a city I had never been to, in a house on a hill overlooking a green with a steepled church. It was a dense but tree-lined residential neighborhood which spread twinkling away from the balcony's vantage point. I gave up and went home, but soon returned by car. Reports trickled in that no one had shown up for the band, who had played to an empty warehouse.

I grew so upset that I started packing a bag, when I thought, well, what if this is all just a dream? After all, my friend from Mexico had looked different, as though I had imagined her presence. I asked my roommate, who was skeptically watching me pack, where my man had gone. She blushed and said it was not her place to tell me. I told her it was her duty. She said he had left with his other girlfriend and hadn't she already told me about this girl? I remembered then that she had, but could summon no clear image of the other woman's face.

"Men are dogs," she said. "But at least you didn't give a concert and no one came."

13

The concert hall was sunken into the hillside. It looked exactly like the museum with the basement bookstore where my parents used to take me sometimes. Same light blue carpet, same sweeping staircase, pouring out into a vast lobby, like a fish tank for a whale.

I had gone to attend the World Festival of Sacred Music. Getting to Long Beach was relatively uneventful, but trying to get home would have made a convincing Surrealist comedy. At one point, I gratefully recognized a friend working at the t-shirt counter. She looked miserable, in danger of being eaten alive by the throng of concert-goers pushing for merchandise. When she saw me, she just jumped over the counter and left the job behind.

We figured on catching the bus or maybe a train out of the park. The bus stops back in the city were no more or less convenient than the train stations, but I have an imposing fear of being in a subway in earthquake-prone Los Angeles. I joke about it on a regular basis, and pretty much have myself convinced that if I ever do enter the subway system in L.A., I will actually cause the Big One.

While we were standing there figuring it out, a very mean and toad-like woman emerged from behind the ticket booth. She slowly uncurled one long, bony finger, and aimed it at the bus pulling away from the lot. That's when she told us the bad news, that was the last bus leaving, and no more trains either. My friend and I looked at each other, looked at the bus, looked back at her, and took off at a run. We caught up easily, due to a mild traffic jam, and boarded.

Of course, we hadn't bought tickets. We knew we would eventually be asked to produce some, but in the meantime we were at least moving in the desired direction. We laughed, guilty and a little nervous, about the thousands of people finding out at that moment that they were stranded on the mountain due to lack of public transportation.

The bus slowed down around a curve, giving us a long look at a 7-11 parking lot with hundreds of people in it. Only a half a mile from the park, they had obviously walked down. We noticed another one of our crew, there in the lot smoking a cigarette, leaning up against her famous blue and white van. We jumped out before they had a chance to ask for a receipt.

The van was all crappy inside, full of clothes and magazines and assorted furnishings, but I didn't care. I settled into the front seat for a nap, while the others went inside for supplies. Just as I'm putting out my pre-nap smoke, a huge, scary transient with matted hair and wild eyes pops up at the window. I knew the window was open, so I had my pepper spray in my hand before I ever closed my eyes. I kept him at good distance with that while I locked the doors and rolled up all the windows. He was trying to find a way in to the van. I just started screaming right at him, waving my arms and waving the spray, until he ran off. The drive home was improved by the junk food.

14

Criminals have a way of looking like everyday people, even while they are about to commit armed robbery. This is something important to keep in mind on the job as an undercover cop. After all, blending in is part of my technique, too. I'm wearing a black suit, fancy leather boots, big Jackie-O sunglasses, hair coiffed in a loose knot, suspicion of rust-colored lipstick on a slightly pouty mouth. This is the uniform in the very posh jewelry store I'm guarding. We must have had a tip it was about to be robbed, because a whole team is being deployed. I'm the only one here so far. It's mid-afternoon, and we didn't think they'd try anything until closer until the end of the day. The store is packed with customers. Wait, make that customers and armed felons who just looked like customers.

Suddenly everyone has a gun. My commander and some back-up are just strolling in when the robbers pull out the guns and start to yell orders. I drop behind the balustrade on the mezzanine where I had stationed myself, and listen to the instant chaos that erupts downstairs. My commanding officer is up on the balcony with me, she's shooting at the bad guys. I reach for my gun and it is definitely not there. I don't have one. Damn.

The balcony is made of wood beams, not quite wide enough to use as permanent shields, so you have to keep moving. I hang between two beams, watching my Amazon blonde bombshell commander pick off criminals on the floor. Bullets fly in all directions, except from my hand, which holds no weapon.

I see an opening in the melee and run down an outstretched corridor made of stone. It is open along one side, like a cloister walkway. I'm up on a high floor, and as the corner rounds, the view opens down into a courtyard. I see that the building folds in, forming a square around this courtyard, with the open archway all along it. I can hear the bad guys pounding along behind me, and so I sneak down into the yard, which is littered with benches and large stone enclosures like the marble tombs at the Lafayette Cemetery.

I hide in some deep shadows among the tombs, and there I find my lover, seated on a wooden barstool, looking up at the building and wondering if anyone can see us from the windows. He pulls me to him and we make love. I climb on to his lap as he sits on the stool, our clothes are transparent, not material. We are naked for each other. When we finish, I take the long way around back up to the catwalk. I try to discover the spot, to see if he lingered there, but it is all in shadow. I did not wish to stay in one place for too long, as it was considered unlucky. In leaving, the memory started to fade.

On the walk home alone, as usual I take a shortcut up the hill from Main Street. I have to walk close by a neighbor's house to go through the yard there, but they recognize me, so it's not really trespassing. I start up the incline, when a man calls out to me from the sidewalk just behind. I am standing in the spotty shadows under an elm tree in the afternoon. Pellets of sunshine on soft pale yellow grass. He yells, "Do you know what time it is?" I tell him, he steps forward and says, "Would you like me to fuck you with this?" as he holds up for me to see a huge piece of splintered driftwood.

In his other hand he holds a book, with the legend hand-written "Serial Killer 125 Since Spring". I am about to turn and run, but I realize he could overtake me. Two steps away I see a shiny new garden tool, a curved fork claw thing with a weathered wooden handle and four or five sharp tines. I pick it up and show it to him. He turns and runs off; I continue up the hill toward home, with the garden claw in my hand.

My apartment building is a dormitory, where my friends and boss lady are gathered. No one seems to really care about my near-mauling, and this is irritating in the extreme. Finally, I spot someone who will listen, and I start to tell him the story. I know the attempted pervert's name is Mitch or Frank, and I have his phone number as well as the serial killer book. I still need to call the cops, though.

Well, this guy had listened to me so then the decent thing to do was to go and look at slides of his new paintings. It was only fair, I suppose. I sat on his lap and our faces were very close, and he kissed me. Impulsively, or so I believed. A lovely kiss it was, warm and slow. My mind's eye cut to a close-up of our lips sliding, and his hands on my back. I could watch it like a film, and feel it on my body at the same time.

We move into the bathroom, to be alone. The white tiles are wet and cracked, and we sit together and make out on top of the washing machine. The room opens on one side to a deserted sweep of beach. A rainy day in winter, off-season for the tourists, cold even for the locals. The bathroom is a disaster of dirty plates and bottles, piles of wash, and dozens of pairs of shoes in a heap. I feel uneasy when I look at the steely ocean, so I busy myself counting the things in piles, kissing him with my eyes open.

15

New York City had a beach, and the only way off the island of Manhattan was one big bridge that brought you to a bank of ferries taking cars and people across the bay. Well this day was the Apocalypse, and the traffic was outrageous. One hundred thousand cars, two hundred thousand more sweaty pedestrians with backpacks.

We were standing on a promontory with the main bulk of the city behind us, in a small stretch of park. The cliffs swept away toward the waves below us, and the bridge emerged from behind another tongue of land at our right. Its serpentine swell mirrored the land's contours as it rose, a quarter of a mile out at its farthest point, several hundred feet in the air out over the bay and dropped back in to the little port tucked in the next inlet. From there the ferries to the mainland launched. Why anyone would want to be stuck in a traffic jam at the end of the world was beyond us.

We turned back toward the city, looking for a place to have dinner. A friend of ours was having a party, but he was charging for the food and drink. How lame was that, I thought. I mean, it's the end, you know, share for once in your miserable life. I got really irritated and became short-tempered with my girlfriends. One of them had a speedboat I tried to escape in, but my lover ran up to the beach and talked me out of it. He said I'd be shot due to the panic and chaos at the border. No more ferries, the bridge traffic hadn't moved in hours, it was getting ugly.

On the walk home, with the beer and egg sandwiches my lover had bought for our dinner, it occurred to me that I should be more forgiving of myself and others. Then it occurred to me that it was much easier to be forgiving when I had a beer and an egg sandwich and warm, strong man with his arm around me and the city is wet and quiet but not destroyed. Much easier then than when I am hungry and tired and broke, and I'm thinking damn this could really be It, and where is he, the bastard, am I going to die a sap at the end, missing him? Looking for him? Yes, well. It's always easier to forgive once everything works out.

16

Botany was not my best subject in school, and this plantation was making me nervous. It was under attack, and the animals had to be saved. Shiny black and green snakes were scooped up into two bags, and loaded into my car. I raced out of there at top speed, driving like crazy. The road became a roller coaster track, distorted blacktop curves with perfect yellow paint and I took the wrong exit because it was the closest, but it was not the way home.

The road went sharply up hill and culminated in a breaking wave made of shaved blue ice. At the top of the wave was a temple of Bacchus, fully attended by beautiful women who traced my skin with handfuls of ice. We gathered around a metal obelisk embossed with strange glyphs, which was being used as a phallus in some sort of ritual.

Awhile later we—we being me and the trunk full of snakes—were back on the road. In the home stretch now of a long drive into the desert. The desert that in the movies always hides the secret research facility around the next bend in the valley road. There I found a long, low house at the end of a long, straight driveway. It gained its privacy not by walls or screens of rock, but by distance from the main road. Inside waiting for me was a scientist who had agreed to take these snakes from my care, as our own facility had been destroyed in the attack.

I planned to leave right away, but I found this strange man charming and fell in love with him. I rubbed his shoulders while he sat at the piano. He didn't play, but sitting there relaxed him. I conceived a child and when it was born, it was my teenage sister. Her eyes were glowing blue, like a Castaneda scout, and this worried me deeply. I ran from the house, not in fear, but in complete certainty that it was time to leave. From above, I watched myself take the long road on foot.

17

There had been a storm during the night, and when I finally reached them, the streets of my hometown were covered in fallen branches and boughs. An abandoned red rowboat had been bolted to the side of the converted stables at the end of the cul de sac. The barn had become a stables and then a four-star restaurant, scattered with romantic tables at discrete intervals. Blonde wood, white cloths, candlelight. "Knife Four" or something, it seemed clever at the time. One lap around was all I needed to hate it.

Back outside in the cool night air of Venice Beach. Trees in Venice grow straight out of the sidewalk. I was leaning against a car doing my makeup, when the car started to pull away. It was a black car like an old-timey super-hero hornet car. A young and beautiful couple were driving it, and talking about a party at their friend's, to which I happened to be on my way as well, so we went together. The girl disappeared as we approached the complex, a dark concrete fortress at the beach near the edge of Windward.

Inside was a concrete bank of payphones, all in use by people I felt I knew. There for the party I figured. But they could have all been calling cabs. The hurricane had picked up its pace outside, and it was too windy to walk. All I could hear as the elevator doors shut was a couple yelling over the wind or over their minds, Why don't we love each other anymore?

18

Someone else's car is always an adventure. Driving up a pathway that seemed idyllic, along an ocean. A pathway that spiraled in upon itself as it climbed. The cliff below had been cut with deep stone stairs into the living rock. At the apex was a flat shelf which the car could not manage, so it had to be abandoned. I started out walking back down the stairs, pulling the car along behind me, bouncing like a child's toy.

Back on the ground, a plaza in my hometown was crowded with people watching a video on outdoor television monitors. In the crowd was one man I knew, who invited me to come over to his studio. I half-heartedly agreed, knowing I ought to be getting back to my grandmother's house. As I imagined my recriminating aunt, I heard her over the phone on my voicemail, talking about how disappointed everyone was that they had only seen me in the morning. I started down the road toward the house, full to overflowing with my extended family.

The kitchen in my grandmother's house is separated from the living room by a feature wall open on both ends to direct the flow in circles: kitchen-dining room, fireplace-living room, foyer-kitchen. My mother looked very young that day, like we were the same age. Mom was trying unsuccessfully to get some sleep on a sofa bed in the living room, piled high with comforters and crisp white pillows. Across the room a section of the wood floor in the foyer was being devoured by termites. I got the can of Raid from under the kitchen sink, and started spraying them. The can made a noise and a spray which woke my mother up. I apologized to her, but kept it up. It wasn't working. The spray ran out so I shook the can, and sticky poisonous foam flew everywhere.

19

One of my teachers in high school was a real player, but in that special sleazy way that involves an oversize comb in the back pocket at all times. Somehow I managed to have a crush on him anyway, which was pretty funny and slightly humiliating. I tried in vain to get his attention, and now he shows up uninvited in my memories at times like this, when I feel rejected and invisible.

Earlier today I was walking down this street near my grandmother's house. It was on the other side of the bridge over the railroad tracks, farther up the hill. I was with some of my old posse, and some strangers as well. It's a nice wide street, tree-lined. Residential enough that they don't even bother painting a center line. Big houses on either side. At the very top of the hill was a gate that hung open, granting access to a white gravel driveway that led up and around to a private house not visible from the main road.

It was built in a coliseum style, with an outdoor colonnade that had amphitheater seating overlooking a pool at the bottom of an artificial cliff. It was maybe 100 feet down to the water. The pool was clear and blue, it looked like the ocean. I remembered an earlier time that I had gone swimming down there, and as I was trying to pinpoint the memory, my teacher, whose house it was, came over to sit by me. He started kissing me and then he started going down on me; and he was being really voracious about it.

I rather enjoyed it, which is odd for me. Especially because it was so obvious and there were all these people around and we were out in the open. I threw a towel over my lap with his head there, so even though it was still very clear what was going on, at least it wasn't completely exposed. One of my girlfriends came over to us and just started talking to me. I'm pointing down at him trying to shoo her away without disturbing him.

When she finally left I turned my attention back to the water below and for the first time noticed it contained a shark, as well as a couple of these seriously mean looking, scary, blood-red man-of-war jellyfish. They were huge, like human size or bigger.

I freaked out, going into a miniature panic when I realized they must have been in there while I was swimming around. I realized my ignorance of them had protected me. If I had panicked, they would have sensed the fear and come for me, weak prey. They were undeniably lovely, the way they float with purpose, but they hummed like death. It made me wonder whether it is better to know the source of your fear or not. Confidence and serenity are good defenses. Worry over peril leads to poor decision making.

20

Christmas that year was celebrated on the front lawn at my mother's house. A living conifer was strung with lights and ribbons. Around it some household furniture had been arranged—two long wooden benches in the shape of an L, an assortment of coffee tables, and end tables with lamps on them, plus a radio. The side of the house had been removed which opened directly onto the kitchen, now a three-walled room. This, I later understood, was so as to be able to hear the phone if it were to ring.

In neat rows emanating outward from the base of the tree, presents were arranged in either red or blue paper, according to size. It looked like a carpet made from rows of dozens of identical boxes. It was unsettling to note the lack of spontaneity in gift distribution, but none of us were children anymore, after all.

I was seated on one of the long benches, with my back to the road, next to my grandmother, who was going on and on about Hanukkah. All the candles and the oil and blessings and who knows what else. The phone rang in the kitchen, tearing mom away from this religious conversation she had been enduring, to answer it. From outside, we could hear over the line the sound of children singing Christmas carols—phone carolers. Turns out, they were the kids of the Disney CEO.

How it happened to be Christmas in the first place is kind of a long story. Earlier that day at the police station, where we all work, we were looking into a murder. A dead body had been found lying on top of an old Chevy under six feet of water. Seems the whole block had been flooded. Someone saw the girl from a boat on the surface, figured she had been down there too long.

Turns out she had been handcuffed to the car, and left there for some unknown reason. We surmised whoever cuffed her was not expecting the flash flood, and may even be remorseful over the tragic developments. It didn't take long to find the car's owner. Exactly as we thought, he was only going inside a shop for a few minutes and wanted her to stay put. While he's inside, flash flood. Dead girlfriend. All very depressing, especially for a holiday.

We arrested this guy, who was much nicer than one would think given the circumstances. He felt terrible about it all, I'm sure. We let him think about it overnight in jail, on suicide watch, while we all went out together to have a little drink. I changed my clothes first, putting on a long cherry red velvet dress and apple green velvet coat, and slung a toy shotgun over my shoulder. When I was jolly enough, I went over to mom's place.

To find the living room on the lawn. But I knew better than to ask any questions, it would only be an excuse to escalate. So instead we opened presents like everything was perfectly normal and absolutely commonplace.

Of course, stranger things had happened in our family than this. Just the other evening, I took my mother with me on a ride to the moon in a paper airplane. We lifted off from a cul de sac in the neighborhood. There were only two houses at the end there. The very last house was announced by a patchwork sprawl of chain-link fences, different heights, different weaves and metal plating. This so-called fence was allegedly to hold back the huge German shepherd that lived there, growling and sniffing me enthusiastically.

Our friends were gathered in their yard, next door to the dog house, to watch me and my mom go. In this friendly house were two men, my lover and my former lover, who had just formed a white-boy hip-hop band together. This situation was unacceptable to me, but hilarious to most of my friends, so it went on.

The trip up to the moon was not what I expected at all. We put the top down on the shuttle, and even with a sweater it was pretty cold in space, like October in New England after a rain. The sunset beyond Asia over our shoulders looked like a fireplace, with planet Earth smoldering in its grille.

Our approach took us straight out at top speed. When we reached a point where our entire vision was taken up with the glowing full moon, we banked hard right, swooped upwards, banked left, and cut the throttle. We coasted gently across the face of the moon at a snail's pace, lingering in front of it in silence for an eternity. By this time, the sun had come up between our feet, and they—

the moon and the sun—were drawing together in the sky, as if for a kiss.

We were face to face with the moon at the moment when the sun sneaked up behind her and disappeared. A total eclipse. Her face went dark, but with a halo made of gold and resting on a scarf of silver. It was majestic and romantic. I berated myself for taking along my mother, thus wasting such an ideal dating opportunity. Beautiful, though, to witness up close what is meant by the music of the spheres.

When we landed back at the house, it was clear there was a raging party going on in the backyard. People were draped all over the front steps and walkway, a drummer was keeping bad rhythm with some guitarists and a drunken spoken word singer. That would be my drunken drum-playing ex and my drunken apocalypse poet current boyfriend. Perfect. Mom had the best idea—she just went home. I was tempted to go with her, but loathe to be a bad girlfriend, so I hugged mom goodbye and went inside.

21

Vacations are often cut short by work emergencies; these "emergencies" rarely turn out to have been so serious. On this particular Sunday morning, I was still scraping sleep sand from my eyes when I arrived at the studio. Everything and everyone was in place, no great mess beyond the usual disorder of a working painting studio, and no one so much as appeared tense.

Two questions swam in my hungover head. First, What was such a big deal that I had to rush right over? Followed closely by, Something in here is different, what the hell is it? I got the answer to the second question, and it ruined entirely my interest in the first.

I looked up toward the ceiling, and registered the addition of a gigantic crystal chandelier, affixed at the apex, under a skylight. It was monstrous, grotesquely elaborate, and dangled unconvincingly from one thin hook. It ought to have been throwing a dazzling kaleidoscope of prism rainbows in every direction, but it swung mute. There was a strange trick of ambient light that made the surfaces seem to shimmer on their own, without the benefit of a direct light source, but more like glitter that refracted light.

I don't remember if I screamed out loud right from the start, or if it took a few moments for sound to come out of my contorted face. The movement of the glass surfaces was caused by the literal movement of thousands of tiny baby spiders, silvery gray ones. I freaked out so completely, I truly believed I was going to die of shock. As soon as I recognized them, they swarmed off the chandelier and fanned out onto the ceiling on every direction, headed for the walls. Paranoid or not, I was pretty sure they were coming for me.

I have never run so fast in my life. I can remember the sound of my bosses calling to me as I turned tail and made my escape. I think in that instant the others did not yet realize what was happening, but they stopped calling and laughing quite abruptly so I think they figured it out.

I didn't feel the need to send in a resignation, I felt my intentions never to return were clear to everyone.

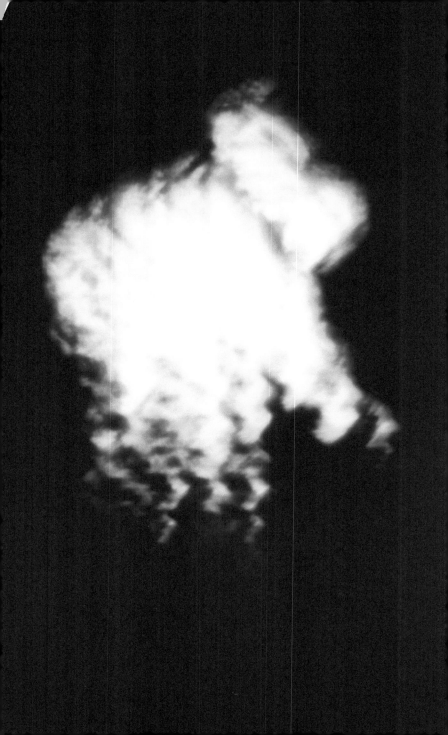

22

My first time in a cross-country train was eerie, but I was prepared to travel alone.

Suddenly, there was my best friend occupying the seat behind me. The train was exactly half-full, so that everyone had a window on one side and an empty place on the other. Even people traveling together were seated individually for the time being. I vaguely remembered that she had been there all along, but that fact apparently hadn't sunk in until this moment.

The train was passing quite close to the freeway, crowded now with midday traffic. We were so close, it was as though the track were just another lane. A red or blue car was overtaking us. Driving it was my old roommate from college, with her younger sister in the passenger seat and her daughter of seven in the back. The daughter was leaning forward, poking her head up between the seats in an effort to participate in the adult conversation. She had one elbow propped against the back of each seat, and swooshed her little blonde head from side to side hyper-attentively. All three were laughing, white teeth shining and tanning-parlor faces thrown back, loose curls blowing in the wind. They sailed right past the train and on into traffic.

When I lost sight of them and returned my attention to the train's interior, I noticed a friend/love interest from my neighborhood had boarded along the way. He came straight to me and in greeting, licked the side of my face. He was sporting a drastic mullet wedge——the most blatant hair don't I have ever encountered. I couldn't bear it, so I returned to contemplation of the view.

The train was a tandem set-up with two double-decker lines, two tracks wide. The parts facing each other were completely glass at some points, with the result that from my seat I could see down into the dining car, below and across from me. It was full to overflowing with the most audacious variety of desserts I have seen. I could see several buffet tables and half a dozen dining tables, all burdened with pastries, cookies and cakes. Sweets were literally piled in heaps everywhere I looked. The arrangements were Grecian somehow, subtle but over the top. There were candelabras and lush draped fabric. A few women were eating from their laden plates, gazing limply at the country going by, oblivious to my spying.

By then the train was gliding to a stop at some sleepy station in the middle of Nowhere. Everyone had time for a little walkabout. At first I was going to try a low profile, get some alone time onboard, but this very snide and slightly stupid girl appeared and sat directly across from me in the berth. She had barely settled in, the strange little bird, when she started complaining. Everything from my cigarette, to my feet up, my newspaper out, my lunch on my suitcase up-ended at my knees. Done with that, on to the glare from the open shade and the smallness of train-brand pillows, and the distance to the dining car, and the heat out on the platform. Her voice was shrill, and she spoke with no particular audience in mind. Not to herself, but addressed to the universe generally, as though everyone would and should be equally outraged by the oppression to which she was being subjected.

Her father was seated across the aisle, looking guilty and tired. I stared at her hard, amused for almost ten solid minutes before I reached out without warning and punched her hard in the throat. While she was still gasping, I reached around to the back of her head, got a handful of hair, and slammed her face forward into my lunch. She fell to one side, floundering. Dad said nothing. I took that walk.

The train emptied directly onto the landing of pale gray and pink stone stairwell, overgrown with bright green tufts of long grass. Wide, flat steps led up and around, to an exit or entrance not visible from the landing. It distinctly did not seem man-made; it was the very definition of picturesque. The arterial flight ran through a deep hillside, so it took a few moments to arrive up above.

I emerged as one emerges from a womb. My eyes first, level with the ground, and adjusting to sudden sunlight as my head floated up to the height. A vast carpet revealed itself, made from the same long, bright grass as spotted the stairs. The motion of my approach made it seem like a waterfall of green light.

The field took shape as a wide yard, with a house at the far end, maybe 800 meters away. The distance between was laced by a meandering stone pathway of smooth pebbles of the same rock. The grass was the color of limes when examined up close, and it was full of tiny purple and white flowers, and fallen leaves from the eucalyptus trees that lined the walk.

Closer to the house, the path widened into a delta area, a driveway I supposed. More trees formed a dense wall of privacy and shade that ran from the end of the path down a short hill to the street below. The street sloped down toward a bit of a town, which I could just glimpse between tree trunks. I saw a moose walk aimlessly around the square, headed vaguely toward the train station. The end of the last car of our train was peeking out from behind it into the intersection. Traffic was lining up on both sides of the barrier. I had the idea of returning this way, as it seemed shorter and I was thinking about the time.

From where I was, I had to pass by the house fairly close to get down to the road. There was a large kitchen window, the kind with thirty-six small panes of glass and verdigris framing. Through it, I could see two women talking heatedly at a wide wooden table. I would have just walked through the yard to the street beyond, but the way was blocked by a score of large white poodles, identical in every way, all tied to the house with leashes that reached all the way across the driveway to the trees on the other side. No way around them, and they looked mean and creepy, not cute at all.

I thought maybe I could ask permission from the women, so the dogs would leave me alone as I passed through. As I approached the window to knock, I was at first waving politely, then frantically, having no luck getting anyone's attention. I realized that the discussion at the big wooden table was now a full-fledged argument, becoming violent rather quickly. Either they were very cross with the blackberry pie on the table between them, or the pie was the unfortunate bystander, but they were both stabbing it with knives for emphasis as they fought. I went back the way I had come.

At the top of the stairs descending down to the train, I came upon my best friend in deep conversation with a man we knew from school, someone I never cared for. That piqued me, but once inside I was so overjoyed to find that girl and her father had vanished, that I forgot about it immediately, and settled in for a nap at sunset.

When I woke up, I thought for a second we were at my stop, so I got off to check. It turned out not to be—mine was next—but I saw my lover at a cafe across the plaza. I was intending to meet him at the next station. He had on sweatpants and a dinner jacket, and was seated with three other men, all drinking wine. I crossed the square to find out what was going on. Of course, as I did so, my train left without me.

This was not so great a tragedy as it seemed. As I soon discovered, the bar they were in was actually itself a train, going on, after a short stop, to the same destination, and scheduled to arrive sooner. That was his reason for being there, he had come to surprise me at the station. It took a great deal of effort on my part to remain calm through the process, but it was very important to me to hide the true depth of my neuroses from my lover, sensing his absolute need for serenity and egolessness. In the end, we waited together for my train, and I got my bags just fine.

23

None of us were really sure why we were all gathered in the neighborhood bar that night, but when we realized we were going to be in there for a while, I went to fetch my car. By the time I pulled back into the parking lot out front, it had snowed over a foot. Everyone just stopped where they were and left their cars for the night. It was thick; I could barely see the neon signs only a few yards away.

We stayed in there drinking for a while, eventually we closed the place down. Outside, traffic had started moving again, and I saw that where I had parked was actually the middle of the street. Several other people had made the same mistake during the blizzard, and we were all being towed. I came out just as they were starting to pull mine out into the road and away. I made a run for it, leaping up onto the running board of the tow truck, my arms wrapped around the side view mirror. The driver was sufficiently freaked out that he ended up just giving my car back right there.

It was a good thing, too, because my boyfriend had a meeting at midnight with some very shady characters, and we didn't think it would be wise to be late.

24

A police safe house, a truck and a young boy to protect. When most people think safe, they think big strong walls, razor wire, guarded check points. In truth, a safe house is often safe by virtue of its subtlety. A suburban street in the foothills, just one of dozens in its development. Real families live in the area, making a child less obvious were he even to be allowed outside.

The whole hill overlooked a broad valley with snow caps at the far end, their white pointy heads melting into cloud cover. All the houses I could see were white, with a handful of red ones among them. Fire stations, maybe. It was a loose grid of bushy tree-tops and colonials. Up where we were, the houses and the money were both newer. We had found a modern design, the kind that's really just a big concrete block. Perfect.

We also had a full hook up media center, satellite TV comes with the house or something. I was one of only two agents who stayed permanently in the house. The other being my boss. One agent would come in and out every day in the disguise of a maid. If they needed a quick consult, someone would dress up as the UPS guy and come to the door. The satellite TV in combination with the long nights indoors had me resorting to stealing pot from the commander's stash to smoke while he slept.

I promised the boy a baseball game every time he needed to focus. He was not as good as I was at savoring the fear of knowing someone's out to get us, that they'll kill us if they find us. My fears were largely offset by our preparations and our skills, in which the boy had no confidence. He wanted his parents. I remember I used to want mine, too.

One night nearly a week later, from the couch I hear someone trying to break in. I was in the habit of making a show about going to bed upstairs and sneaking back down. I only caught a glimpse of the man at the patio door before he gave it up to try the kitchen window, but that was enough. He was wearing a suit and tie, so not a robber. Time for skills.

I slipped into the kitchen to wait for him, since I was pretty sure he'd get in that way if he had any breaking and entering experience. I waited until he was all the way inside the house, with only one foot still on the window ledge. His hands were balancing his weight on the edge of the counter. One more second and a fluid motion would bring his whole body around. Just before that was the moment of his least poise. I killed him with a knife thrown from across the room that lodged itself in his forehead. He looked so surprised.

25

A hotel, the kind you can find in any recently liberated Eastern Bloc city. Decorated with the intention of appealing to a modern international crowd, but looking more like a second rate hotel near Madison Square Garden in 1970, it was all fluorescent lights and dirty linoleum like stone ground mustard. Brown carpet and framed posters of museum exhibitions. The ceilings had crown molding whose contours were dulled by years of overpainting in lead-based Antique White.

Across from our suite was a landing in the main stairwell, which wound its way around the elevator shaft like a mahogany boa constrictor. Down the hall to the left were a small service stair and elevator, mostly used by porters and other staff. I had come back to the room to collect my dear friend who was a guest at the hotel. I lived in town, but he had insisted on staying here, so as to make it more of an adventure, which he claimed to sorely need.

As was our habit with each other, I simply entered the room without knocking. I discovered him shirtless and barefoot, pacing around the quarters with his hands pressed to the sides of his head. He was looking at the ground and taking long strides with heavy footfalls, and in his right hand was a gun.

He was clearly in acute emotional pain, of the sort that is not physical but is so profound you nevertheless feel that either your heart or head will explode from the pressure. In the room already with him was my best friend, who had completed our trio all through university and for a little while afterward. She had had to move away, too. This weekend was a specially appointed reunion.

With no provocation I could make out, he began wildly gesturing with the revolver. He yelled some, too, but not at us. I did not feel that he would actually harm us, but I was losing confidence that this mood of his would pass without incident. I sat on the bed, my girlfriend on the sofa opposite. He paced between the sitting room we were in and the bedroom beyond.

The television was on in there, a local news program was interrupting a prime time sit-com for a special report. The volume was just too low to hear properly, but certain keywords floated through: body of a girl, police at this hour, suspects, citywide search, no apparent motive, identity withheld pending notification of family...

The cordless phone was on the dresser closest to me. Several times I tried to edge closer to it, but he was never out of the room long enough to make real progress. Finally, I saw a break in his movements and made a dash out of the room. The main stairs were too wide and well lit for a pedestrian escape, and I had only seconds to plan a route.

I headed through the swinging doors to the service stairs. We were on the 124th floor, a long way down. I took the stairs two at a time, even jumping down entire flights. I would feel the liftoff and the fall but my knees were taking the impact so I kept on running.

I made it to the lobby level and was running headlong toward the concierge intending to call the authorities. The corridor was lit from the far end, giving it the look of a tunnel, and several figures in silhouette were advancing. Policemen. I ran at them and tried to rush them on, but I soon noticed my girlfriend was with them. Apparently, she'd taken the elevator.

I wish I could remember more about the poetry my dear old friend was reciting to himself as they led him away. He went peacefully, having put his shirt and shoes on while we were fetching the cops. He knew what to expect, and gave the gun over without being asked.

26

A weekend professional retreat was being held in the city where we already lived, not far from our neighborhood. Some of the retreaters had signed up for a tour of the big national bank offices. Ours was one of those allegedly progressive work environments, with no real walls or doors; a big open space opening off the lobby corridor. A vast circular reception desk sent visitors bouncing off into the space like pinballs.

To the left a deceptively small door led to a long schoolhouse hallway. Beyond the desk a second doorway led to the labyrinth of offices allowed to have doors of their own, probably for client comfort level. To the right a vast area spread out from the desk, veers out, around and back in toward the desk. It's like a cross-section of a blimp, and it could hold a whole football field, with the corners cut off. It was carpeted and lit diffusely, incredibly quiet although absolutely bustling. The majority of the hall was a fully functioning supermarket, with a cafe at the far end.

Our group had thirteen, and we split up to observe consumers move through this hybrid space. The cafe was packed, it was lunch-time, but a few of us tried to settle in there for some hard-core people watching. I overheard someone talking about the yoga class in one of the school rooms that afternoon, so I left to check the time and place. It took quite a while to navigate the maze of bulk buy corn chips and upset display carts of canned soda. I made for the little door on the other side of the vast reception desk, and went through it.

I entered a long, empty hallway, unmistakably institutional. Polished but aging linoleum, pale yellow walls made of large shiny bricks, doors made of wood with the top halves windows of reinforced glass. Behind one of those doors, I found him. He was stretching, waiting for the class to assemble. He kissed me and picked me up off the floor when he hugged me, so that my body and hands slid down his body as he loosened his hold. Despite his warm welcome, I had already decided that yoga would make me too tired to have a proper bachelor party that night, so I left.

It took me a while once I found the exit to find my car. I hadn't driven there, I had walked from my nearby home, so it became a question of putting the night before together and deducing where I had left it. Once behind the wheel I felt better, more in control, though the narrow streets were parked in to the point of impassability. It took a good 15 minutes (during which time I perpetrated a forgivable hit-and-run on a dozy blonde who cut me off in her haggard Volvo) to go a total of three blocks to the freeway ramp.

Entering the highway, I realized that a few of my girlfriends were riding in the other seats. My best friend's ex had been boasting about walking on the freeway home, and we were trying to catch up to him to check it out. We saw him up ahead, not struggling along the shoulder, but right in the center lane, walking at about 50 miles per hour. Good for a pedestrian, but I still had to swing around to the right to avoid running him over. We waved, and I accidentally pulled into the exit only lane, so I had to swing back to the left to stay on, and narrowly missed him again.

A few miles later we arrived at our destination—the bachelor party. Inside were more women who had taken the yoga class and were, as I predicted, tired. All the boys had gone out to a bar to watch the game. They were expected back soon, giving us some time to get ready for the big night ahead. I was giddy with anticipation.

27

The Apocalypse was coming and all my friends were having parties. Two of my best friends were having big shindigs at their places, which were on opposite ends of town. I was irked to have to go back and forth like that, but it was a special occasion, the last ever occasion really, and I didn't want to miss either one. Finally, as I rushed down the street to get back to my best friend's before it was too late, I see the fireballs. Lavender and pink and orange like sherbet, the sky filled with them, and by the time I got back to the castle, it was over. I was so upset to have missed the End like that. Worse than getting stuck in a taxi on 10th Avenue at midnight on New Year's Eve.

By the time I arrived at her place, every single guest had passed out on the floor at their last known position. Every one of them was exactly as drunk as you would expect them to be for the Apocalypse. Snoring and drooling drunk. My friend was awake though, and she wanted one last martini almost as badly as I did. Of course, not a drop of alcohol left in the place.

She lived in half of a renovated Catholic school. It was all Gothic stonework outside, all 50's linoleum and fake wood paneling inside. Over my shoulder, I catch sight of a table on the lawn outside. Absolut Vodka had sponsored

a party for the occasion, Absolut End, and there, on the
table, was a half-full bottle of Absolut Kurant, glistening
with condensation from being so cold in the scorching sun.
I hatched a plan.

The main obstacle besides the bartender was how to
get outside. I had to sneak through the rest of the building
to get to that lawn. A serious mission, but I went for it. I
made it through the dark hallway, down the main stairs,
and part way down the hall to the back door. The lights
were kept off in this wing, and only one guard roamed all
its halls, so it wasn't that difficult to proceed undetected,
until I neared the end.

People appeared from doorways off the corridor. This
wing was narrow and lit only by fluorescent lights. They
all wore white lab coats, and the guards were armed. I was
not supposed to be there. I crept through a swinging door
into a room humming with the sound of a hundred hackers
talking to themselves as they composed code. Futuristic
metal consoles with red and blue flashing light displays
make excellent cover when you have to sneak through a
room of hyper-focused people wired on so much caffeine.

I finally make it out the door at the far end of the
library room. The bottle was still on the table where I last
spied it. I told the bartender he was urgently required at the
loading dock, and he ran off, leaving me to watch the bar.
Well, that backfired on the poor guy, because I grabbed
the Kurant and two other bottles and headed around front
to go back inside through the kitchen door, the safe way.
I was very proud of myself, and celebrated with a round.

28

After-hours in a seedy place in New York and/or New Orleans. My lover and I are faced with each other across a gray formica coffee table with chrome trim and a red leather horseshoe sofa. A clock over his left shoulder continued to read 1:50, as it had for hours already. We had to leave at 2:15 to catch our planes, but I was not all that concerned. I did think it odd to have such a big, round, flat, white clock at an after-hours club, where people go to cheat time.

The club also has an art gallery, and I went to check it out before we left. A bouncer with big meaty arms flings one across my path, barring me from the back rooms. I try to pass him, but he casually ignores me and I cannot budge his tree trunk. Finally, my lover walks in right past me, and tries to pull me through. After a moment, this strategy works and I am past the ropes.

I embark on a hazy labyrinth of artists, velvet sofas full of cigarette burns, paintings of naked women, exploding-star wallpaper, and green lights. We soon spill out onto a deserted street on a movie backlot. Garbage floats past like giant cellophane butterflies, in the wind blowing off the river. Some strange men watch as I back my car around the corner through an intersection against the light. I squeal into the alley, my lover hops in, and we speed off for the airport.

But first we stop at the mechanic my friend recommended, for an oil change. A punk rock casualty looks at the car, and when he's done the hood won't close properly. My lover waits outside as the punk tallies up $800 worth of repairs, already performed. I see the bill and start to cry, because my grandmother only gave me five hundred, and my rent is due. I strike a deal to pay half now and half later. Though I still can't afford it at all, at least this spreads the disaster around, plus buys me some time to work it out.

While I was inside, a troupe of African dancers and artisans had set up a miniature festival on the lot outside. There was music and tribal dancing, but it stopped and cleared out the minute my lover got out of the car. He looked straight at me and said, I don't love you anymore. You're here and she's there with me and that's it. I'm sorry if I hurt you.

"Oh," I said. "Okay."

29

I wandered off the road and into a valley. Often, this sort of place looks quite green from far and turns out to be golden-sere upon closer look. This valley was the opposite; it glowed yellow from a distance, yet grew more lush and cool with each approaching step. It was long and narrow, glass-flat on its floor but shaded as much by the old trees as by the steep hillsides which rose straight up from the ground. All I remember clearly about my first weeks in that cranny of land was feeling out of place. A real city slicker had come to rural America.

My husband was a dear man. He was a gift from the gods in many ways. He liked me at first sight, found our differences intriguing rather than frightening. But the thing I liked best about him was that he had a name. None of the others had names. He was much older than I, in his sixties. Such a gentle face, like an angel's face reflected in a river; wrinkled, certainly, but more like clouds than leather. When I met him, he was at the long end of sadness. I was a poem, written expressly for himself, called "First Happiness After Years of Melancholy".

There I was in my vintage swing dresses and beaded cardigans, standing out like a red lace bra at a church picnic. Many of our neighbors were widows who had

had designs on him for years. I feel certain that I will
never be able to imagine the depth of the bitterness they
expressed in private. I could feel it rolling off of them like
fog in my presence, but I was insulated by the warmth of
my marriage.

I rarely encountered their ire head-on, mainly because
I preferred to stay at home. I have no idea how many
days floated by like yellow butterflies on the breeze. I
would sit on the wide verandah that wrapped around the
entire house. We lived in his family home, a rambling old
farmhouse with lots of windows and fireplaces, and history.
Outside were pots of bougainvillea, the only pink things in
the whole valley. There were lemon trees, too, and white
dogwood, ivy on trellises, pampas grass along the many
paths. I would sit, as I have said, on the verandah, and
watch him in the gardens, moving my seat every so often
so as to follow his progress around the whole property and
never lose sight of him.

One day, he was in the roses. He straightened up and
waved to me, blew me a kiss, and slipped to the ground
like an unzipped silk dress. I was beside him in an instant,
but it was too late. He was dead, the doctor later told me,
before he ever hit the ground.

Never before or since have I felt such a profound sense
of loss; it permeated everything. It was like a chilly, foggy
night with the windows open. Everything was damp,
including the air in my lungs, and it was hard to tell the
outsides from the insides of things. The next few weeks
passed, slow and cumbersome, in the dark. Numbly, I
received kind words, or more often, casseroles, from an

endless stream of my recent persecutors. No one is gentler in your sorrow than your enemies, once their hatred has been sated by your misfortunes.

The happiest time of my life was the not-quite-a-year I spent in that house. Before I left, I took steps to make certain the house would stay in my dead husband's family. He had a son, my age, who was traveling and whom I had never met, but I had never wanted for myself what should be his. I left during the night, with a note on the door I closed behind me, "Thank you all for your very good casseroles—I washed the dishes and left them in the kitchen for you."

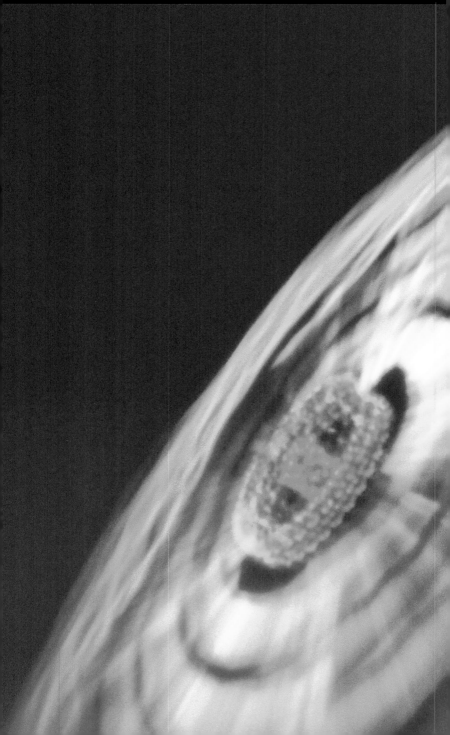

30

Skateboarding on my stomach, at lightning speed, propelling with both hands and feet through a corridor of studio spaces which open behind fire doors painted red and orange. The view is majestic like an ancient city, down into the industrial artists ghetto, aflutter with red flags hung from shiny steel girders.

Behind one of those banners is a nightclub straight from the 1940s. A polished dark wood wrap-around bar torques up alongside a carpeted stair. Women wear pearl chokers with three or four strands and heavy diamond clasps. Their eyes are drawn with smoky charcoal and smolder in the shadows of their beaded hats. The thick carpet absorbs sound, bringing it down to a sensual murmur. When I enter, I am a little girl looking for my father, who is a regular in this speakeasy.

As a reach the landing of the stairs, I see myself seated at the far end of the bar. A female Buddha in her forties with a gleaming clean shaven head and a watery red silk jacket. I turn to watch myself enter, and buy myself a drink.

31

Gingerly picking my way along the path through the woods behind the house, I am leading my mother's family on a backyard tour of L.A.'s rich and famous. I recognized the house because of the old brick wall whose crumbling remains will be preserved and incorporated into the renovation plans of the new house and grounds. I know about these plans because I was in the habit of sneaking into the house and spying on its occupants from the attic. These woods look more like the path to Young's Pond adjacent to my grandmother's property in Connecticut, but it's L.A. alright, no question about that.

We made our way down the short but steep bank to the river. The water level had apparently risen a great deal since my last visit; my customary sitting ledge was completely submerged. Instead, I sat down on a freestanding toilet, behind a door in the middle of a clearing. It struck me as slightly absurd, since there were no walls, only the single door in its frame, and this toilet. A man peered through the door, standing ajar, and handed me some papers to sign, a contract.

32

A cruise ship was our final destination, my stepfather and my friend the photographer with her hyper-intelligent cat. I was driving a rental car by myself on this road trip, and I exited the highway too soon, and started down the narrow road along the widening bay.

At a certain point I could drive no farther, and, as I started to wonder about insurance claims on rentals, I arrived at the harbor landing, all modern architecture like that terminal at JFK. My photographer friend, with her cat under her arm, was looking for the penthouse suites, because that's where her patron, the one that gave her the tickets, had his state room. Before we could settle in, she insisted on finding and studying a map of the ship's exits, to avoid confusion later.

While she was studying the map, which was really just a degraded fourth generation xerox of a line drawing showing the layout of the rooms, I turned to look at the way we had come. Behind me stretched an absurd length of the flat upper deck. Beyond the stern the dock pulled itself away like a 3D movie, as the ferry turned its attention toward the bay.

I don't recall the precise moment when I realized we had boarded the wrong boat. I only remember that it suddenly seemed like everyone else had slowed way down while my body and the boat continued racing on. My car was stowed on the other boat, the right one. After making some desperate inquiries, I resigned myself to taking the long way to meet it. That is what you get for seeking out a slower moving society in the hopes of relaxing. The difference in travel time was now to be measured in days instead of hours.

On the first leg of the long overland journey to our intended port of call, my companion and I are riding in the backseat of a car driven by my stepfather, deep in conversation. I can see her lips move, but her words do not make noise, and then she is my grandmother. We continue to talk in normal tones, as the back seat splits in two and the halves drift apart into separate lanes. I am in my own car, exiting the highway and following an increasingly narrow and less paved road along the edge of a spreading delta.

By late afternoon, the rutted dirt road had become impassable. I stopped to survey the situation, and discovered I had come around a bend up a steep hill along a high embankment. The sallow dirt to the left of the road sloped toward the wide flat river. To the right of the road stretched a meadow of long golden grass, into which I waded. I closed my eyes as I walked, letting the nuances of sunlight direct me. My eyes opened to reveal the highway rushing toward me like a javelin, and billowing out behind me like a pilot's white scarf.

33

Driving North on the Pacific Coast Highway between the Palisades and Malibu, there is a good stretch of road where there aren't many houses. Just the cliffs that rise straight up to higher than a driver can see from his side. Unless you were in a convertible, like I was. I could see the cliffs' sharp green edges, at nearly right angles, where the hillsides' gentle slopes had been sliced like the heel of a loaf of bread to make room for the highway. I swung around a bend and relaxed into an unusually long bit of straight roadway—almost two miles without a curve. No other cars in sight, either.

To the left, the road dropped off toward the water, in a continuation of the hills' interrupted contours. The crashing waves below looked crisp, cold, and salty. I felt rather than heard each one break. Lulled a little by the momentum of my speed, the rhythm of the surf, and by the brave little flowers growing in the crevices of the hill, I was in a trance. I suddenly looked ahead and my heart lodged in my throat. An enormous bald eagle with gleaming gold beak and talons, crystal blue eyes and a glowing opalescent crown, swooped directly at my head. He came within an inch of my face. I could feel the warmth and a fine cedar smell in his wake. He had careened up at the last possible second and disappeared behind me. I hit the brakes and scanned the sky for him, in vain. Eventually I just started back up the coast toward my destination, the Chelsea Hotel.

The Chelsea was a beachfront hotel, with wide dark wooden stairs that led up to a half floor on the South end. There were two rooms up there, and that is where I always stayed. It had a little vestibule full of my things, which I never bothered to lock inside the rooms, per my arrangements. I had an understanding with the management. I was coming back in from watching some of the biggest waves I can remember, and a hard wind was up, too. I took my top off while I was still in the hall walking toward my rooms, my breasts were snow white compared to my tanned shoulders.

I was mildly shocked to see the old man emerge from the hall closet and hurry past me, down the stairs without a word. He was more flustered than I was. I tried to dismiss his image, knowing my lover must already be inside there waiting for me. He said he has a surprise, some old pictures or something of mine my grandmother had him bring over to show me. I had cut my walk short to make it back in time to look at them before dinner.

There we were, on the big soft bed, sitting cross-legged facing each other. Filing my entire life away, all the years broken down into still shots. We fell asleep right there among the pictures, his hand resting on my forehead like a benediction. Our conversation threads its unbroken way from waking to sleeping. A black milk crate stuffed with hanging file folders marked with names, of lovers, places, and years. He went on handing the pictures of my life to me, one at a time, not rushed at all but not slow and lingering either. There was no damp sentimentality or cynicism. It was an effortless conversation, a task to be completed but not relished, emotional, but not trite.

It all gets filed away, sorted; my life in pictures I don't remember being taken.

34

The theater of the school was packed, despite the tempting afternoon sunshine on the green outside. I had a front row seat for my lover's stage debut, Romeo to someone else's Juliet. I was trying very hard to be happy for him, his talent was obvious to me as well as everyone else in the audience. I admitted to myself that he was too convincing, but I never allowed myself to actually wish he would fail. The seat next to me was occupied by a former lover with his new girlfriend, a black woman with jade green eyes that were launching daggers in my direction.

In the row behind us are two women in full-tilt Park Avenue regalia—Chanel suits, bulky jewelry—who would not shut up about the quality of the acting, how the boy must really be in love with the girl, and so forth. I will the new girlfriend's daggers to bounce off me and stab out Ms. Park Avenue's eyes. I turn around, and remember I'm in the front row when I see four hundred people staring over my head. The two women are me and my best friend, very old.

The second act of the play is starting. Some Gregorian chanting with half the cast on stage facing out and the other half standing in the orchestra pit facing the stage. Great acoustics, as their heads are lifted, ignoring the hymnals they carry. Chaos erupts as it so often does, without warning. But this orchestrated chaos revealed itself to be modern dance. I think back to the casting session with my friend, the play's director. She had to see how every potential actress looked in diaphanous dresses. Now I see why.

After the performance, we all find ourselves back in the dorm, drinking. The dorm is my grandmother's house, but much larger. I'm trying to take a shower, but my friends are mixing drinks in the bathroom. My skin was so dry it even felt dry under the water. I must have dozed off standing up because a knock at the door startled me awake. Everyone else was long gone, but here comes my lover, still in stage makeup, asking if he can join me to wash it off. He does not ask me what I thought of the show, or of him. He just holds me with his head on my shoulder and I wash his face in silence. Later in bed, I think, I'll tell him how great he was, and how proud of him I was. But I never do.

35

I had to sneak out of bed one night, to attend a secret student league meeting in the catacombs under the library. To get there, you had to take the secret door out through the men's room. A narrow staircase wound around so tight that the light was gone in a matter of steps, and it wasn't for another twenty or thirty feet that it appeared again at the bottom. A long, damp tunnel just high enough for an adult to walk upright extended back toward the library. I supposed it ran underneath the big wide lawn that stretched between the library and main building, with another hulking structure full of classrooms and antique fixtures to the right.

It was a fair bet that this underground network was rarely used. It was wet and musty, lit only by whatever portable light sources people had with them. The dim flickering I had seen from the bottom of the stairs was coming from a group of people holding flashlights. It was difficult to make out how large a group we were, as all but the ten or so main organizers were hovering in the shadows beyond the inner circle of students. I didn't really ever have a chance to get my bearings.

All I remember clearly is someone whispering to me that one of the people in the group was a spy, and so we weren't going to be discussing our real business that night, as a precaution. Turned out to be a good idea, because someone makes a joke about offing the editor of the newspaper, and Bam! The dumb-ass narc starts trying to arrest people.

I ran back the way I had come, up the stairs and out across the lawn, and it was amazing because it was the first time I had ever tried to run, and it was so easy. I could go very fast. I was flying over the damp sidewalk, barely touching its surface. I looked down and saw my feet in blurs, no molasses slowing them down. The grass had an eerie blue quality to it in the heavy mist, like seaweed.

I ran around to the front and up to my room above the library, and barricaded my door behind me. Pulled the drapes shut, turned out the lights and television, and waited for them to come. I was sure they had been right behind me. Miraculously, my lover was not at home, and so would be spared the imminent melodrama as well as his punishment for our relationship. At least guilt about that was not on my list of concerns.

I must have dozed off with the gun in my hand, because when I started awake, the whole campus was being shut down; students and teachers were being gathered in groups. What group I belonged to I didn't quite know, but it was clear that I was in a group being efficiently exterminated. I was led outside, told to keep my eyes on the ground, and boarded a ship of some kind. The backpack I had on was searched for weapons as I entered. I couldn't remember what happened to the gun, and I didn't want to bring up the topic.

It had been some time since the others and I were allowed to carry cash, so I kept mine hidden in the pages of my composition book. That's why I grabbed the backpack when I had the chance. They weren't taking our possessions away yet, perhaps in an effort to conceal the seriousness of our situation from us, so I carried the forbidden cash close to me in case I was lucky enough to find a guard who could be bribed. A whole day inside one large spaceship, it was all orange tile and curved surfaces with recessed lighting and open spaces. Metallic voices gave orders in soothing disembodied tones over invisible speakers.

I sneaked from one condemned group to another, always moving further back in line. But the lines were getting shorter almost as fast as I was sneaking. I waited to be found out, and listened to a voice coolly give directions. No guards in sight, and not one other person even looking around for a chance. It seemed like I was the only person trying to live through this. I asked myself, was it death itself or my need to hope and fight which was causing the fear?

36

We were all supposed to gather for some big show, down at the neighborhood beach, the small one by my grandmother's house. Way more people than were expected showed up, so the whole hillside and sea wall were dripping in spectators. Down at the edge of the water, a pair of pom-pommed cheerleaders in red and yellow began to move. Soon they were joined by dozens of others.

Just a few minutes into their routine, we started noticing the water. The tide, instead of languidly lapping and retreating, was steadily advancing. It was creeping forward, slowly but undeniably, like it was quietly reaching for something. Of course, the cheerleaders were the last to notice, what with their concentration and having their backs facing the water. People started leaving. The girls got confused and some smiles faltered.

Just as the first girls were getting knocked down by the surf, it began to rain. The tidal waves were coming in horizontal and vertical. I was amazed that no one went to their aid. Myself included.

ROSS
OF THE
ROADS

r

37

My two best friends and I, a boy and a girl, went camping in his dad's RV. Not far outside of town, just over by the lake, where it was quieter. She was in love with him and wanted my help to gauge his interest; I was supposed to contrive to leave them alone at a certain point. She made it clear to me that this was my solemn duty as her friend.

But on the drive up, he takes me aside and tells me in confidence that he's gay. He swears me to silence, of course, including with regard to our mutual friend, who was in the gas station bathroom at the time. The two of them are not really that close except through me. My personal theory was that he suspected her crush and was afraid she'd spread the rumor to clean up after the rumor of the crush. And if it got around school, it would get back to his father, who might very well beat him to death. So there we were.

It didn't take long, only a few hours, for her to start acting pissy; shooting me dirty looks whenever he couldn't see her face. And I can't tell her why, and he's forced me to take a secret vow not to leave them alone together. He was right about her. Her ego would require spreading this information, compounded with the temporary stardom of being the bearer of such juicy gossip. Damn.

I'm not sure how she managed to drag him off down the beach, or exactly what happened there, but I can guess. At some point, he had told her. She ran off toward town, freaking out as predicted. Apparently she was swearing undying hatred for both of us. Frankly I didn't see why he had to tell her I knew already, and was helping keep it from her. That only made it worse, because it blocked any interference I could run.

We pretty much knew she wouldn't be coming back, so we took off after her, hoping to beat her to town. We needed to get to his dad before she had a chance to. Apparently, she had threatened to go straight to him. I had to admit that I did not see this coming from her, even as self-involved as she was. We were both shocked, and hardly spoke the whole run back through the creepy shortcut in the woods.

We ran all the way to his house, but we saw him driving away in his truck as we came up through the back garden. The shotgun was in the rack. We turned on our heels and headed back the way we came; we arrived at the clearing at the same time he pulled in. He saw me but my friend was hiding down the path, so the father and I just stood there eyeing one another for an eternity, waiting, I suppose, for something to happen.

All in an instant, my friend leaps out from behind the RV; he had sneaked around back like some kind of Ninja. He whacked his father in the back of the head with a big dead branch, knocking him to the ground and greatly confusing him. We tied his hands and feet and tried to decide what to do next. I couldn't believe it. It felt like we should kill him, because that's what they do in the movies that start this way. You know, kill one person's parents and the teenagers split in the camper and have a road movie. We've all seen them. But instead we stood there smoking cigarettes and thinking hard in silence.

We pretty much couldn't kill him. Besides the ethics, there was that irritating girl who could link it all together at home. But we didn't have high hopes for talking reason to him either. We rolled him into the camper and my friend drove it away, while I followed in the truck. We drove back to the house and parked the truck in the driveway, pulling the RV around back where it was hidden from the street and the neighbors. We planned our speech for when he woke up, convincing ourselves it would work out after all. And both thinking we still might have to kill him tonight.

Gradually we realized he wasn't showing any signs of waking up. We had been standing around in the backyard, smoking and drinking a beer, talking. After a couple of hours with no movement or calling inside the RV, we went in to check on him. That's when we realized he wasn't breathing. He was totally dead. So we untied him and rolled him back into the house, put him in his favorite chair and called 911.

We told the police we got bored in the woods and had come back in for the night two hours earlier, pulled in out back and gone for a walk in the garden and stayed outside. We were coming in to get warm and found him there; we had no idea how long he'd been like that. The truck was here earlier, but we didn't even stop in. They believed us. The girl never said a word, because she thought we killed him and she was too scared to gossip.

Funny how things work out.

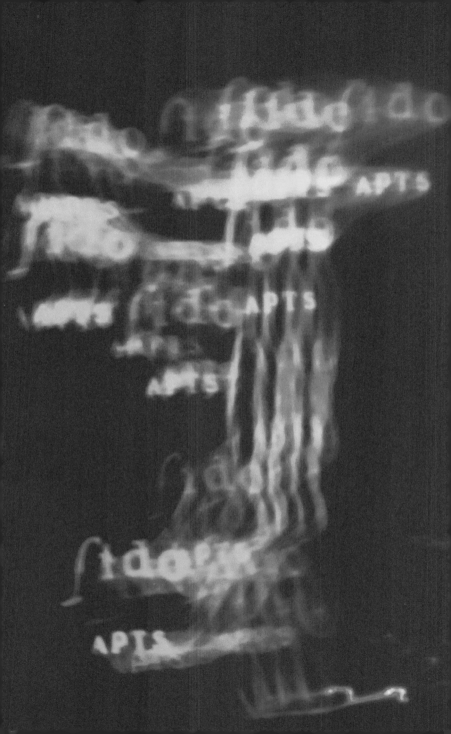

38

Then there was the time I cut off my own penis and tossed it into the pond behind the embassy. It made the long walk back around the grounds a lot smoother; and I felt much lighter and distinctly carefree for the rest of the evening. The grounds were lovely, with a marble walkway around an enormous cloister. Around the perimeter and in the center of the courtyard were reflecting pools, but the outer ran off in places in little rivulets into the cultivated woods. My little penis swam away in one of those.

39

"Underground passageway to Field F." What a strange way to get from here to there. Especially since we had to go in socks, no shoes.

Catacombs of highly polished black and gray marble opened into a lavishly appointed reception area, fed by several tunnels. We were directed through one which seemed to be the largest. It in turn opened into a wide reception area like a giant restaurant hostess station. It was an old underground cathedral which an artist had converted into a studio. Tonight, it hosted a catered black tie function for the city's art elite. I walked toward the host, with the noise of a crowd in polite conversation swelling up from beyond.

I was back at the beginning, at the first reception station. Resigned to the long walk back to the party, I was joined on the road by a big, burly Hell's Angels type, stuffed into a rented tuxedo. Apparently, he considered us to be friends, since he was very familiar with me. I stiffened when he embraced me, hoping he would get the message. As we walked along, the sidewalk split. I thought it might be an opportunity to separate from my new companion, but he guided me up the steeper of the paths. I became concerned when I did not remember this part of the journey from the first time through, but was distracted by the epic view from the bridge we were crossing.

A harbor city cascaded toward the bay on my right, blending fluidly into the water, as inlets and ships staggered along the curved shoreline, blurring the boundaries of ocean and land. It was so detailed, I felt I could see the flowers on people's kitchen tables. It was so far, there was no noise but the rush of wind.

We turned and had arrived back at the studio cathedral entrance. I had planned on ditching my new friend at this point, but that seemed irredeemably cruel. I was a respected figure in this crowd, and I vouched for this man who obviously loved me. I caught sight of a group of friends at a table by the front, and joined them. This clearly was the choice table, as it had a direct view down into the stage. The stage was pronouncedly lower then the mezzanine where the guests were seated, and lit dramatically. A performance was in progress, insipid music and some dancers in leotards.

Besides my friends, many others who I did not recognize were with me on board a massive ship, like a cruise ship but without the joy. It was docked at a bridge in the middle of the city. I had been chosen with several other girls to get lifted by swinging elevator car across the channel to the far river bank. We were wearing bathing suits even on this cold night. A fact which I forgot as soon as I saw the word, written in red letters on the side of elevator car number nine, Death. I stood breathless with shock as though I had been punched, as a naked girl was dumped into the freezing black water from this car.

Running along the deck back the way I had come, I was blinded by tears of rage as comprehension gathered itself. My companions from the banquet were huddled over coffees at their small table by the handrail on the upper deck balcony, with a view of the harbor channel directly below them. They looked intensely miserable, but I did not stop for them, because they looked guilty as well. I heard one comforting the other that nine could not possibly mean Death, as they two also had tickets numbered nine.

I paused for one nervous moment, catching my reflection in a polished metal plate on the wall. I heard a voice in my head rehearsing how to explain that I should not be killed like the others, because my mother isn't even Jewish. But I realized something. One Jewish parent is enough to be killed for, and I was not about to renounce my heritage for the pleasure of these sick fucks. Death seemed noble to me for the first time. No, that's wrong. My own capacity for nobility revealed itself, and gave me strength. I turned and deliberately walked into an open car.

As the car swung over the water, it pitched sideways and I fell out, into the dark oily channel. When I came up I realized there were dozens of girls in my situation, treading water and too cold to cry. We were subtly being swept by a current toward a low bridge, whose concrete column supports were submerged; the waterway flowed between them, but was blocked by screen drains. No apparent escape that way—we were being rounded up in the water.

One beautiful girl in a black swimsuit made it up out of the water and into the street. She ran and ran, back toward the building and out of sight. I heard shouts and then nothing. The chaos caused by her escape provided an excellent diversion for my own attempt, which I began to plot.

40

I came to in an upstairs room, a chateau bedroom. It was cavernous, hewn from solid stone and furnished with lush, overstuffed couches covered in rich fabric. Diffuse light gathered from several directions—a fireplace, a chandelier, a candelabra across the room, and a window which was deepening to a darker shade of blue as the setting sun made its way around the house. I had no idea where I was in the world, but I was not dreading the evening ahead; the house simply radiated pleasure at my presence.

I stuck to the carpets as I moved about the room; the flagstone floor was like ice on my bare feet. Donning the silk pants and sweater waiting for me on an ottoman by the fireplace, I started to look around. First, to the window for a view of...what? Whatever would be out there, I suppose. I could see the moon rising over the rim of the hills at the horizon. Few lights twinkled in the indeterminate distance to the hills; few hints were forthcoming at all in that direction. But I did surmise from the lunar position that I was facing East.

Armed with that fact and only faith besides, I arrived in the library on the ground floor to find my lover. He was stretched out like a cat on the copper velvet sofa, in front of another roaring fire in a hearth the size of a Volkswagen.

He was absently caressing his two vampire fangs, his mouth
hanging slightly open, his eyes contemplating the cherubs
on the ceiling. Wearing jeans and a black turtleneck
sweater, he was irresistible.

I lay down with my head on his chest, his arms
wrapped around me holding a blanket around us both,
woven through with the pattern of a hunt. It was the
warmest place I have ever been. We communicate without
speaking. I hear his voice in my head so clearly. When I
turn to see him, the firelight bounces off his marble skin as
it would a statue. His glistens.

Inside my head and his, I am all but begging him to
let me stay. He is trying to get me to leave the house, to
go and never look back. He wants to protect me from
himself. Of course, the more he insists, the more firm I
become in my decision to stay. The couch faces out on one
side toward a courtyard at the center of the house, with
a cloister-style arcade running around it. We could see it
was raining hard. In any case, I think to him, I won't be
leaving in this rain.

In fact, I won't be leaving ever. I love you and I want
to stay with you and if that means becoming like you then
so be it. That is what I wanted, at that moment, more than
anything in my whole life. When we kissed then, he let me
feel his fangs with my tongue. He bit it, piercing it easily
and then to my neck. He bit my skin enough for me to feel
the sharpness, but with no intentions for the time being.
He pulled me so close to him, I thought our bodies would
simply crush each other. He pushed me away, furious
with us both. I remember thinking that I was more afraid

that he may wake up one night and leave me, out of some misguided gesture of love, than I ever was that he would wake up and kill me.

I rest my head once again on his chest, where I hear no heartbeat and I think loudly, I love you. Suddenly, he grabs me by the hand and, saying only that it had stopped raining, we went out into the street. We went night shopping. Every store we passed he stopped and bought things for a mortal girl's house—red wine, chocolates, silk clothing, soaps and lotions. As we walked, he was singing to me over his shoulder, or resting his arm across my back, or stopping to touch my face for a moment. He wanted my blood, but he wanted me alive, too.

A few days or weeks later, he confided to me the source of much of his bountiful love for me. I reminded him of everything that mattered to him the most as a mortal man. But I also reminded him of what had tempted him into immortality in the first place—the promise of an eternity of beauty. I was everything he wanted and feared he could not have or worse, did not deserve.

Touching him was like running my hand over Michelangelo's David. At the moment when we kissed, back upstairs in the bedroom, it was giddy like a drug rush, almost a swoon. In this sanctuary of a house, it was nearly impossible to hate myself for the desperation of my move. I briefly thought that I might have done the wrong thing, not choosing my freedom when it was offered. But freedom to do what for fuck's sake? Think about him every day until I die? No choice to make, really.

I was afraid you would come to hate me for sparking this conflict within you. But how much could it possibly matter, when we were the only two souls in the world? After a few months, I began to forget other people even existed. Sure, I saw them when we went out and so forth, but those people were like extras in our movie—more or less invisible. I can honestly say I have never been so happy as I was in that house, in love with that glorious monster.

The last thing we ever said to each other was: I love you. And, I love you, too.

FIN

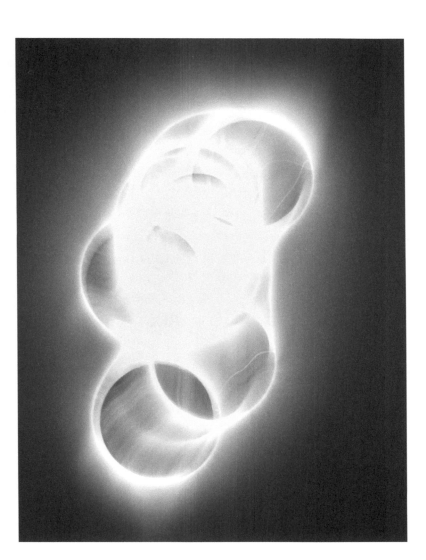

PINHOLE PLATES

California

AUTHOR

SHANA NYS DAMBROT is an art critic, curator, and author based in Downtown LA. She is the Arts Editor for the LA Weekly, and a contributor to Flaunt, Artillery, and other publications. She studied Art History at Vassar College, writes essays for books and exhibition catalogs, curates and juries a few exhibitions each year, and speaks at galleries, schools, and cultural institutions nationally. Her experimental short fiction is oneiric in structure, referencing Surrealist and Jungian notions of a narrative subconsciousness accessing deeper truths. Dambrot is a standing member of ArtTable and an award-winning member of the Los Angeles Press Club.

PHOTOGRAPHER

OSCEOLA REFETOFF'S interest is in documenting humanity's impact on the world, both the intersection of nature and industry, and the narratives of the people living at those crossroads. His parallel careers as an editorial and fine art photographer are characterized by an evocative, cinematic understanding of how scale, point of view, architecture, and motion can express the essence of a given place, often yielding surreal, even dreamlike images. A graduate of New York University's Graduate Film Program, Osceola is the Los Angeles Press Club National Photojournalist of the Year.

Printed in the USA
CPSIA information can be obtained
at www.ICGtesting.com
LVHW060943120923
757853LV00027B/945/J